Builder

Lucy M. George AndoTwin

Mark is a builder. He is helping the Singhs turn their old house into a dream home.

Mark will work closely
with Lauren, the architect,
to make sure the house
is built to plan.

The Singhs have to move out of the house while the work is happening.

They move into the caravan in the garden. They want to be back in the house before winter, because the caravan is small and a bit cold.

It's time for Mark to get to work. He makes some calls and orders all the materials he'll need.

First, the old walls are knocked down with a big bulldozer.

Then, some new foundations are dug out using a strong digger.

A dumper truck carries all the rubble and earth away.

Finally, the ground is flattened with a heavy roller.

Next the materials arrive on a big delivery truck. Mark checks his list.

"That's everything, thanks!"
he says to the driver.

The bricklayer builds new walls. He fetches cement from the mixer to stick the bricks together.

Then he fixes thick foam, called insulation, to the bricks and builds another wall. The insulation will keep the house warm in winter and cool in summer.

Now that the walls are built, the roof goes on.
The roofer has to be very careful in case a tile slips.

Everyone wears a hard hat for safety.

The carpenter fits the new windows and doors.
Soon the house will be weatherproof.

The children wave from the caravan.
They can't wait to move back into their house!

BEEP
BEEP
BEEP

The next big job is to fix solar panels onto the roof. A big lorry reverses down the lane, but then stops.

"Oh no, the lorry won't fit!" Mark cries.

"The lane is too narrow!" Millie, the driver, shouts.

Millie has a plan. She drives off in her lorry and then comes back with a grabber truck.

It has a strong arm to lift the
solar panels onto the roof.

"Hooray!"
everyone
cheers.

Next the plasterer comes
and plasters the walls.

The electrician fits
lights and power.

The plumber fits the new
heating system and hot water.

Finally, the decorating team
paint and lay new floors.

It's just starting to rain when Mark calls,
"Come into the house. It's ready!"

"WOW!" the children shout.
"It's amazing!"

Mark is happy that the family like the house. He puts his raincoat on and says goodbye.

He's got another
job to go to!

What else does Mark do?

Plans and gives advice on building projects.

Puts up scaffolding to fix leaking roofs or chimneys.

Builds brand new houses.

Mends or replaces broken windows.

What does Mark need?

Hard hat

Trowel

Spade

Toolbox

Bucket

Cement mixer

Strong boots

Bricks

Sand

Other busy people

Here are some of the other busy people builders work with.

Architects draw up detailed plans for buildings. They have to imagine every little detail before the building even exists!

Digger drivers have to be very careful with their big heavy machinery to make sure they dig the right things up.

Electricians look after all the wiring, lighting and power on a building project. Electricity can be dangerous so they have special training to make sure everything they do is safe.

Plumbers fit the pipes for hot and cold water and for the heating. They fit boilers and fix sinks and taps.

Next steps

- Mark had a team of people working on the building project. Ask the children if they can remember who they were and what they did.

- Which construction vehicles did Mark use for this building? Ask the children if they can think of any construction vehicles that he didn't use. Talk about different types of trucks and what they do.

- The Singh family moved out of their house while Mark was working on it. Ask the children if they know why and discuss what it would be like inside a house if there were walls missing and builders working.

- Safety is very important on a building site, so everyone always wears a hard hat. Ask the children what could go wrong on a building site. Discuss what dangers there are and how to avoid them.

- Do the children think Mark's job is interesting? Would they like a career as an architect, a builder or a construction worker? What job would the children like to do most and why?

Quarto is the authority on a wide range of topics.

Quarto educates, entertains and enriches the lives of our readers—enthusiasts and lovers of hands-on living.

www.quartoknows.com

First published in the UK in 2017 by
QED Publishing
Part of The Quarto Group
The Old Brewery
6 Blundell Street
London, N7 9BH

A catalogue record for this book is available from the British Library.

ISBN 978 1 78493 728 7

Printed in China

For Granny Wilson

- AndoTwin

For Dylan & Orson

- Lucy M. George